Smelly Melly

Personal Hygiene for Kids and Little Monsters

By Tony Densley and Niki Palmer

Smelly Melly:
Personal Hygiene for Kids and Little Monsters.

Copyright © 2017 by Beanz Books

Authors Tony Densley and Niki Palmer
Illustrated by Muzamil Hussain

First Edition 2017

ISBN: 978-1-925422-15-3

SMELLY MELLY

Max

Emily

There was once a lovely small town where monsters and people lived happily together.

In the middle of town was a school, where all the children and little monsters went to learn and play. They all got along very well and had lots of fun.

Long ago the monsters realised the children were not afraid of them if they were kind and gentle and not scary monsters, so they also joined the school. The children were very friendly and helped them learn something every day.

One day, a new student came to the school. A new monster, to be specific! The teacher asked the young boy monster to stand up in front of the class and tell the class his name. "Smelly Melly," he said smiling at the children and other monsters.

Who would call themselves Smelly Melly? The children were very curious.

Smelly Melly was very hairy and not very clean. His hair had lots of tangles and looked like it had not been brushed for a long, long time. His teeth were dirty, and his clothes were very stained. He also had filthy hands and nails. He was a grubby little monster.

However, when Smelly Melly walked into the middle of the classroom to take his seat, the children knew why he was called Smelly Melly.

Smelly Melly did not smell very nice at all! Everyone could smell his horrible smell.

Some of the children talked together, they knew that they had to do something about this or Smelly Melly would not make any friends and have anyone to play with.

However, they also knew something else; they knew that Smelly Melly did not realise he smelt so bad.

No monster would do this! It was possible that some monsters did not have a bath at home or perhaps Smelly Melly's parents had not shown him how to clean himself properly.

The children decided that they would find out why Smelly Melly was the way that he was. They also agreed that they would help him because the name "Smelly Melly" sounded so mean!

Two children approached him to ask him a few questions.

"Excuse me," said Max, "Why is your name Smelly Melly?"

At his previous school, none of the other children ever talked to him. Instead, they ran the other direction.

"Um," began Smelly Melly nervously. "The children at my last school used to call me that. They said, "that I stank."

Smelly Melly's breath smelled so bad it made the two children move away from him.

"That is mean!" said Emily, then she asked gently "Do you know why you smell like that?"

The little monster had to admit he did not know why?

"No one has ever told me why I smell. The children just said I was a smelly monster."

Now Emily and Max knew that this stinky little monster had no idea that he was so dirty. They knew this was a problem that they could quickly fix!

Bath and Shower

"Come with us," said Max. "We will teach you how to be clean."

The children made their way to the school bathroom where their first lesson to help Smelly Melly, become a cleaner monster, would begin.

"The first lesson is about washing yourself," said Emily. "Do you ever take baths or showers?"

"No," said Smelly Melly. "I don't have the time."

"This is something that you have to do," said Max softly. "When you do not clean yourself for a long time, your body will get dirty and then it will start to smell. But when you take a bath or shower and wash, you will become clean and smell nice, and people will be happy to be around you."

"Oh!" said Smelly Melly excitedly. "That sounds wonderful!"

"First you must wet your body in the shower or bath with nice warm water. Your Mum or your Dad can help to make sure it's not too hot or cold." Said Emily. "Then when you are wet all over, gently rub nice soap all over your body to get rid of the dirt or smell."

"Finally, you rinse off the soap and dry yourself thoroughly with a nice clean towel," Max explained. "I am sure you will feel more confident when you are so clean and smell so fresh."

Washing your hands

"The next lesson is about washing your hands and when to do so," said Emily. Smelly Melly looked rather confused.

"Washing your hands is very important!" said Emily. "You should always wash your hands when they are sticky or dirty or after you use the toilet, and always before you eat. Washing your hands will get rid of yucky germs which can make you and others around you feel sick." "Have you been shown how to wash your hands properly?" She asked. Smelly Melly thought for a moment and then shook his head.

Emily and Max showed their new friend how to wash his hands properly. They turned on the tap. Next, they put one hand on top of the other and rubbed the soap into the hand on the bottom, then switched hands to make sure both were clean.

Max also reminded Smelly Melly "Don't forget to wash between his fingers as well."

"You should also make sure that you always clean under your fingernails. Lots of dirt and germs can hide under your nails, so it is very important to clean it all out!"

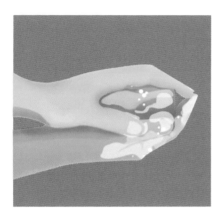  

Emily held up her hands showing her nice clean nails and hands.

"Washing your hands will get rid of yucky germs," said Max. "Some germs are good, but there are many bad ones that will stick to your hands if you do not wash them. Washing your hands not only keeps you healthy but also keeps you and others from getting sick!"

"That is good to know!" said Smelly Melly. "How long should it take to wash my hands?" he asked.

"It's not a race, so take your time, and count to 10 slowly while you wash each hand," Emily replied.

"Remember to dry your hands with a clean towel afterwards too," Max added. "Drying your hands really well makes sure no yucky germs are left on them."

Smelly Melly was so enthusiastic; he wanted to show Max and Emily he could wash his hands properly right now!

So, he began to wash his hands in the sink. He did it just the way Emily had said to do it, and she was very proud of him.

Smelly Melly dried his hands thoroughly and was ready for the next lesson. As he turned to tell Max and Emily, he was so excited to be learning new things they had to back away. He might have clean hands, but he still had smelly breath!

Cleaning your teeth

"Have you ever looked into a smelly monster's mouth?" Emily asked Max. "It looks and smells really, really, really bad."

"The teeth look a little fuzzy, and you can always see a bit of food stuck in the cracks."

"I don't like talking to a stinky, smelly monster because their breath stinks and their teeth look gross," Max replied.

"Their breath smells as bad as a garbage bin."

To help Smelly Melly get rid of his bad breath, Max and Emily gave him a nice new toothbrush that Emily had in her bag just in case she needed one.

The children showed him how to squeeze a little bit of toothpaste onto the toothbrush. "Next you put the toothbrush and toothpaste in your mouth, and you gently brush your teeth up and down so that they are clean of any food or smelly germs," Max told Smelly Melly.

Smelly Melly had so many questions about keeping clean. "How many times a day should I clean my teeth?" He asked.

"Dentists recommend you do this at least twice a day to help make sure you do not get a painful toothache and that your teeth will last for a very long time," Max said.

"OK I will try," said Smelly Melly. "It looks like fun!"

"The teeth in the back of your mouth are just as important as the ones in the front of your mouth even if you cannot see them! You should also give your tongue a clean too because it can also have yucky germs on it.

"So, when you are done brushing your teeth, give your tongue a quick brush too. Rinse your mouth out with water and make sure that you rinse off your toothbrush." Emily added.

Smelly Melly opened his big monster mouth and brushed his teeth just like Max and Emily had taught him to. When he had finished brushing his teeth, his breath smelled a lot better, and the children didn't have to hold their noses anymore or move away when he spoke to them!

Blowing your nose

When the teeth brushing lesson was over, Emily brought a box of tissues to Smelly Melly. "These are tissues," said Emily. "They can be used for lots of things, but they are especially for blowing your nose."

"Wow," said Smelly Melly. "I have never used them before." He explained that he usually just blew his nose out into the air or onto his shirt sleeve. Doing this was so gross the children, ran away from him but again, he had no idea why?

"Blowing your nose properly is very easy," said Emily. "When you have a lot of that yucky stuff inside of your nose, you have to get rid of it, or else you sniff, and sniff, and sniff, and that is not a good thing."

She explained how to blow your nose correctly. "Take a tissue and hold it tightly in your hands. Then blow air hard out of your nose to push all the gunk out. Not only will you not have to sniffle anymore, but it is also good for you to get it all out of your system! But you must always remember to wash your hands right after you blow your nose. You do not want yucky germs all over your hands!"

Because Smelly Melly is so big, he nearly blows people over when he sneezes. The children at school do not like this; they wish he would sneeze the right way.

The correct way to sneeze if you do not have a tissue or handkerchief is to do so into your elbow.

Smelly Melly was confused, they told him not to use his shirt sleeve, and now they are saying his elbow?

If you sneeze into your hand, you will get germs on everything you touch. Sneezing into your elbow is a much safer idea." Max explained. "Got it!" said Smelly Melly. He then picked up a tissue and held it securely between both hands. When he blew his nose into the tissue, it made a loud noise like a horn! He laughed as his ears popped from him blowing so hard!

A lot of green slime came out of his nose, and Smelly Melly was so excited that he blew his nose correctly, he wanted Max and Emily to see what was in his tissue.

While the children found this gross and they didn't want to look in Smelly Melly's tissue, they were glad that all that horrible gunk was out of his nose!

Smelly Melly then threw the tissue into the bin and washed his hands. "Yay" shouted Max, "you remembered!"

Brushing your hair

Some monsters have lots of hair, and Smelly Melly sure does, it's all over his body. It takes such a long time to brush, so he doesn't bother. One day, at Smelly Melly's other school, a big bug had crawled out of his hair in the middle of the lunchtime break. The children ran away and laughed about how birds could probably even nest in his hair, it was such a big mess. Smelly Melly had felt very sad but did not know what to do.

Max pulled out his hairbrush and comb and handed them to him. "Brushing your hair is important," he told the hairy little monster. "You have a lot of hair, so it is extra important for you to take care of it. Brushing your hair is simple! You just have to gently run the brush through your hair from the top of your head to the bottom of your toes."

"Let me try!" said Smelly Melly. However, when he tried to brush his hair, the brush would stick, and it pulled on his hair.

"Ouch! I do not like brushing my hair," said Smelly Melly. "Why does it hurt to brush it?"

"It is because your hair is not clean," said Emily. "When you go home and take a bath or shower you will not only clean your body but wash your hair as well.

Then, when you are out of the water, and your hair is wet comb it first then try brushing it again. That should work!"

"Okay," said Smelly Melly. "Thank you very much for all of your help! I will come back to school tomorrow, and I promise that I will be clean!

Max and Emily waved goodbye to Smelly Melly as he left to go home. Smelly Melly had learned so much today he was a very happy monster, he knew he would like his new school because he had made some lovely new friends.

Once at home Smelly Melly decided to practice all the lessons to clean himself, that he had learned that day. He brushed his teeth, blew his nose, washed his hands, cleaned under his nails, and then took a bath.

When Smelly Melly had finished his bath, he tried to comb his hair. First, the comb got caught in the tangles. After a few hard pulls, it started to straighten out and soon he was able to comb his hair easily! No more nasty knots. Using the tips that he had learned Smelly Melly used the brush and soon his hair was dry.

Smelly Melly could not wait to go back to his new friends and show them how clean he was and thank them again for what they had taught him.

When Smelly Melly went to school the next day, he looked like a new monster. He had never been this clean before, his hair was brushed, his clothes were clean, and he smelled very nice.

He was glad his parents had listened when he got home from school the previous day, he told them about the importance of being clean. They had gone straight to the store and bought all the items he needed to become a clean monster.

Looking and smelling so clean made him feel more confident. He skipped and ran on the way there and whistled a little tune.

He knew he looked good and it made him very happy.

"Wow!" said Max. "You look and smell clean!"

"Yeah!" agreed Emily. "You won't have any more yucky germs, and everyone around will be very happy with the way you smell!"

"This is all because of you guys," said Smelly Melly. "Thanks to you, I feel great! I will be able to talk to other people, and my bad breath will not scare them away!"

"We are happy that we could help you," said Max. "That's what friends are for, to help each other."

In the classroom, all other children noticed Smelly Melly's brushed hair and clean clothes and they quickly went over to talk to him. They were curious about what he had been doing to look so clean.

Smelly Melly told them of his fun having a bath and how brushing his hair had tickled so much he brushed for a long time.

Smelly Melly was glad to talk to the children so he could let them see his clean teeth and they were no longer moving away from him as his breath smelled clean and fresh. He told them about brushing his teeth and tongue and how he could feel how good his mouth now felt.

Smelly Melly noticed Max and Emily smiling at him, and he was very happy he made them smile. He thanked them for their help and told them how pleased he was that the children and other little monsters wanted to talk to him now.

"There is still one more thing that we have to do," said Max.
"What is it?" asked Smelly Melly.

"We have to change your name," Max replied.

"My name?" Questioned Smelly Melly. "What is wrong with Smelly Melly?"

"Does it make you feel good or bad when people call you by that name?" asked Emily.

Smelly Melly thought about that for a moment. "It does not feel good," he said. "It feels bad. People say it in a mean way and then laugh at me."

"Okay!" said Smelly Melly. "But what is my new name?"

"We will just call you Melly," said Emily. "Melly Monster, that sounds like a great name."

"I like that a lot better!" said Melly with a smile. "From now on, I am just Melly, and I am a very clean monster!"

Now all the children and little monsters at school wanted to sit next to him in class and play with him at lunchtime.

"I will take turns sitting by each of you," Melly told them. At this, the children cheered. Melly had never been neater, cleaner, or happier. Finally, Melly had friends...and lots of them.

The End

Beanz Books

Smelly Melly
Personal Hygiene for Kids & Little Monsters

Hospital Adventures Series
Ollie's Tonsils

Alice's Wonderful Adventure to Hospital

Draw a picture of Smelly Melly and you.

Printed in Great Britain
by Amazon